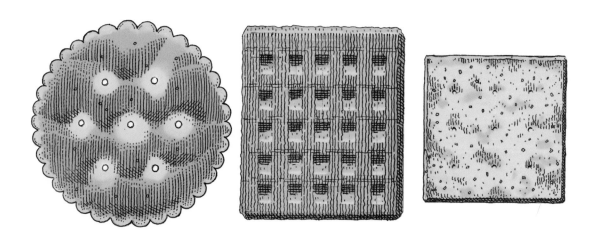

THE TALE OF THE MAGICAL CRACKERS

ILLUSTRATED BY RON BARRETT

STORY BY ANDY CURRIE, TONY LARSEN AND ISRAEL GARBER

D1384840

Lots of Moms get annoyed during the holidays. Mine never did. Maybe it was because we had these big magical crackers in our house.

They'd show up during the holidays every single year, usually on Thanksgiving Eve. A *Ritz*, a *Triscuit* and a *Wheat Thin*. They were the biggest crackers you ever saw. In fact, they were ginormous. The craziest thing was they magically grew back. Even if you only took one little bite.

They lasted
through day after day of
snowball fights.

They stood up
to Uncle Lou's looooooong
"In my day"
stories.

And even our late-night board game battles with friends.

One year, the dog
ate the turkey.

We didn't mind too much...

we had our fixin's.

And our crackers.

Yep, throughout our holidays, those ginormously

magical crackers kept our entire house happy.

Then
there was the year
the giant cheese
showed up,
but that's a whole other story.

Mom's Magical Cracker Recipes

Everyone's Favorite
Bacon-Cheddar Dip
Prep: 10 min.
Total: 1 hour 10 min. (incl. refrigerating)
- 1 container (16 oz.) BREAKSTONE'S Reduced Fat or KNUDSEN Light Sour Cream
- 1 cup KRAFT 2% Milk Shredded Reduced Fat Sharp Cheddar Cheese
- 1/4 cup OSCAR MAYER Real Bacon Bits
- 2 green onions, sliced
  WHEAT THINS Big Snack Crackers

MIX all ingredients except crackers; cover.
REFRIGERATE 1 hour.
SERVE with crackers.
Makes 18 servings, 2 Tbsp. dip and 11 crackers each.

Sweet Dijon Cheddar & Pear Snacks
Prep: 5 min. Total: 5 min.
- 1 oz. KRAFT 2% Milk Cheddar Cheese, cut into 8 thin slices
- 8 TRISCUIT Crackers
- 8 thin pear slices
- 2 tsp. GREY POUPON Savory Honey Mustard

CUT cheese slices in half diagonally.
TOP crackers with cheese slices, pears and a dab of mustard.
Makes 4 servings, two topped crackers each.

SUBSTITUTE: Substitute fruit chutney for the mustard.

Raspberry-Brie RITZ Toppers
Prep: 15 min. Total: 17 min.
- 24 RITZ Snowflake Crackers
- 4 slices OSCAR MAYER Honey Ham, cut into 6 strips each
- 4 oz. Brie cheese, cut into 24 small pieces
- 2 Tbsp. raspberry preserves
- 2 Tbsp. PLANTERS Pistachio Lovers Mix, chopped

HEAT broiler. Top crackers with ham, folding as needed to fit crackers; cover with cheese. Place on baking sheet.
BROIL, 4 inches from heat, 1 to 1-1/2 min. or until cheese begins to melt.
TOP with preserves and nuts.
Makes 2 doz. or 12 servings, two topped crackers each.

Gramma's Secret
Sweet & Spicy Cheddar-Jam Treats
Prep: 5 min. Total: 5 min.
- 6 oz. CRACKER BARREL Sharp Cheddar Cheese, cut into 24 slices
- 24 RITZ Crackers
- 2 Tbsp. hot pepper jelly
- 1 Tbsp. chopped PLANTERS Pistachio Lovers Mix

CUT cheese slices in half diagonally; place 2 on each cracker.
TOP with jelly; sprinkle with nuts.
Makes 8 servings, 3 topped crackers each.

VARIATION: Prepare using KRAFT Pepper Jack Cheese and orange marmalade.